Brain teas

Developing thinking skills

RIC-6412   3.3/137

Jean Edwards

Brain teasers *(Book 1)*

First published by ThinkShop Thinking
Resources Ltd.

www.thinks.co.nz

Reprinted under licence by
R.I.C. Publications® 2008

Copyright© Jean Edwards 2006

ISBN 978-1-74126-718-1

RIC–6412

Additional titles available in this series:
Brain teasers *(Book 2)*
Brain teasers *(Book 3)*

Internet websites

In some cases, websites or specific URLs may be recommended. While these are checked and rechecked at the
time of publication, the publisher has no control over any subsequent changes which may be made to webpages.
It is *strongly* recommended that the class teacher checks *all* URLs before allowing students to access them.

View all pages online

Website: www.ricpublications.com.au

PO Box 332 Greenwood Western Australia 6924

Email: mail@ricgroup.com.au

contents

introduction

This series of three books is designed to provide 5–10-minute activities to 'rev' up students' brains and get them into gear for thinking.

There is a variety of activities aimed at higher-level thinking.

The activites mainly involve language-oriented critical thinking and include:

- **analysing meaning**

- **analysing attributes of words**

- **analysing relationships of words**

- **synthesising rules and creating solutions.**

Some of the activities are oriented more towards creative thinking and problem-solving, involving skills such as:

- **flexibility**

- **elaboration**

- **originality**

- **cooperative work**

- **evaluating ideas.**

www.ricpublications.com.au   R.I.C. Publications®

Name: _____

Date: _____

Listing attributes

Correct Ideas: | Comparing:

Try to picture an apple in your mind.

Then list below all the attributes of an apple which ALL APPLES usually have.

All apples usually ...

1. _____
_____

2. _____
_____

3. _____
_____

4. _____
_____

5. _____
_____

6. _____
_____

7. _____
_____

8. _____
_____

9. _____
_____

10. _____
_____

11. _____
_____

12. _____
_____

13. _____
_____

14. _____
_____

15. _____
_____

16. _____
_____

17. _____
_____

18. _____
_____

19. _____
_____

20. _____
_____

CHALLENGE! Circle the numbers of any attributes which also apply to an ORANGE.

Name: _____

Date: _____

Correct Ideas: | Comparing:

Try to picture a clock in your mind.

Then list below all the attributes of a clock which ALL CLOCKS usually have.

All clocks usually …

1. _____

2. _____

3. _____

4. _____

5. _____

6. _____

7. _____

8. _____

9. _____

10. _____

11. _____

12. _____

13. _____

14. _____

15. _____

16. _____

17. _____

18. _____

19. _____

20. _____

CHALLENGE! Circle the numbers of any attributes which also apply to a CALENDAR.

 www.ricpublications.com.au   R.I.C. Publications®

Listing attributes

3

Try to picture a car in your mind.

Then list below all the attributes of a car which ALL CARS usually have.

Correct Ideas: [ ]   Comparing: [ ]

All cars usually ...

1. _____

2. _____

3. _____

4. _____

5. _____

6. _____

7. _____

8. _____

9. _____

10. _____

11. _____

12. _____

13. _____

14. _____

15. _____

16. _____

17. _____

18. _____

19. _____

20. _____

CHALLENGE! Circle the numbers of any attributes which also apply to a PLANE.

Comparing

Name: _____

Date: _____

Use this Venn diagram to compare the attributes of these two items. List attributes which they BOTH share in the middle part. Think carefully! Remember to number your answers.

SCORE
for correct ideas:

SCORE
for original ideas:

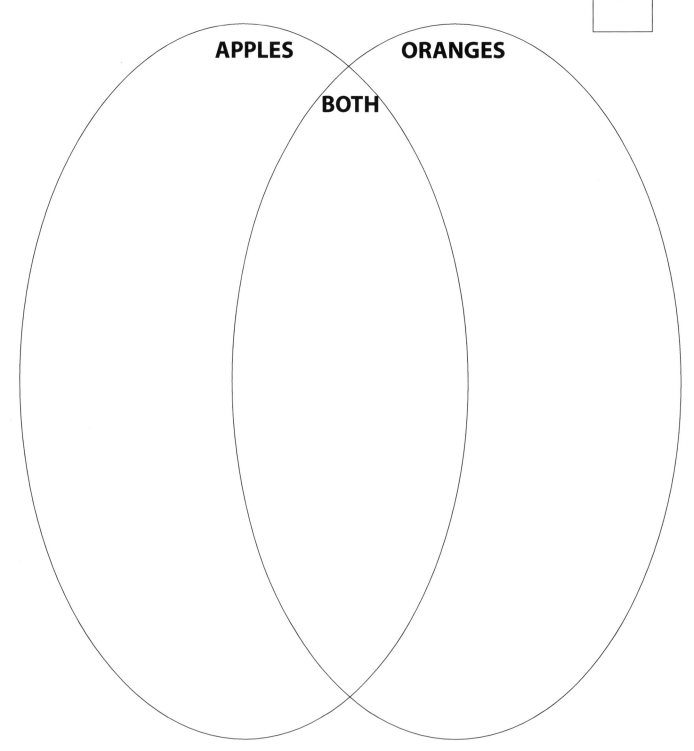

CHALLENGE! Share your answers. How many original answers did you get (ones that no-one else thought of)?

www.ricpublications.com.au   R.I.C. Publications®

STEPPING STONES

Change the following words, one letter at a time, to make the last word shown. Each step must be a proper word!

Example:

Answer:

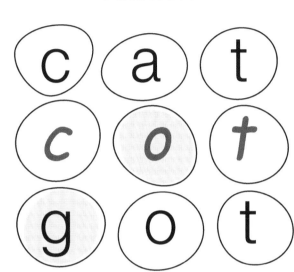

Now you try:

STEPPING STONES

p	i	n
f	a	n

t	a	g
t	o	p

w	i	n
b	a	n

STEPPING STONES

Change the following words, one letter at a time, to make the last word shown. Each step must be a proper word!

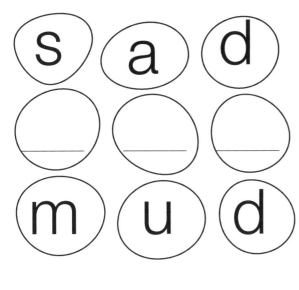

s a d

○ ○ ○

m u d

d i n

○ ○ ○

p a n

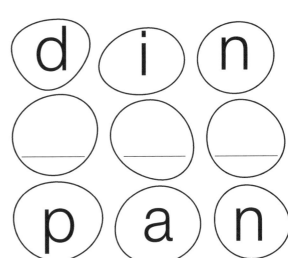

h a t

○ ○ ○

m e t

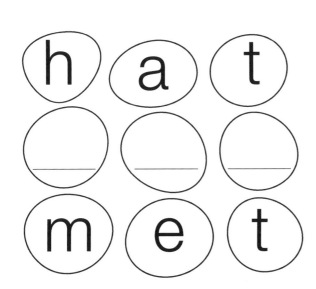

STEPPING STONES

Name: _____

Date: _____

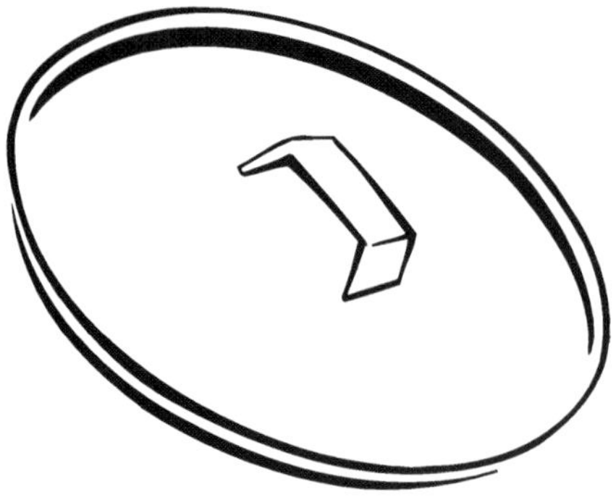

l i d

◯ ◯ ◯

l a p

b a g

◯ ◯ ◯

b i d

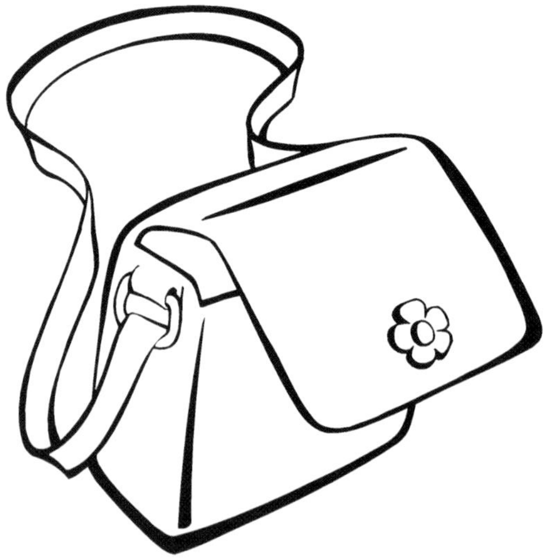

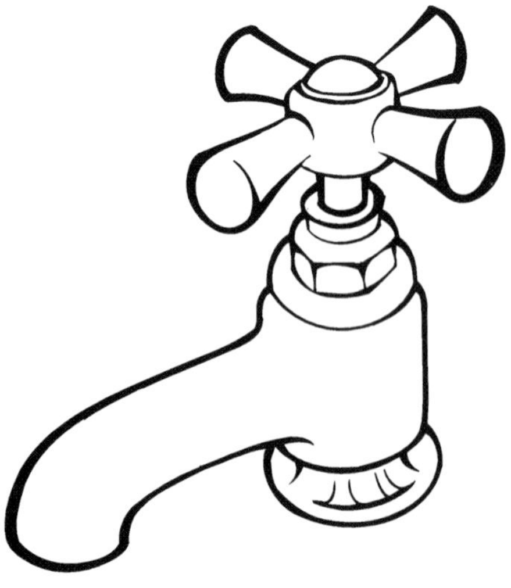

m o p

◯ ◯ ◯

t a p

www.ricpublications.com.au   R.I.C. Publications®

STEPPING STONES

Name: _____

Date: _____

Change the following words, one letter at a time, to make the last word shown. Each step must be a proper word! If you can do it in even fewer steps - well done!

h o p e

○ ○ ○ ○

○ ○ ○ ○

r i d e

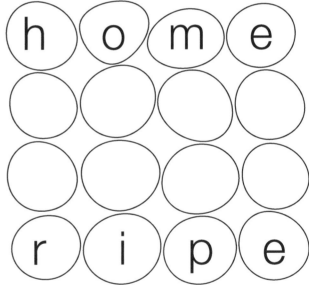

h o m e

○ ○ ○ ○

○ ○ ○ ○

r i p e

w a n t

○ ○ ○ ○

○ ○ ○ ○

c o n e

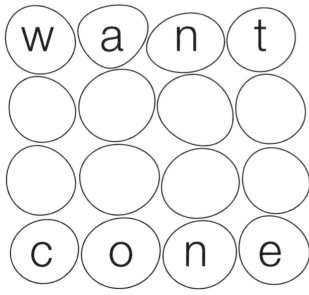

STEPPING STONES

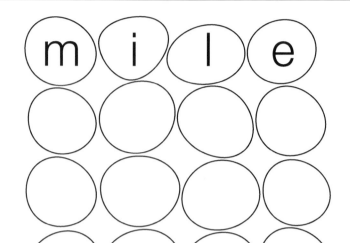

m i l e

h o m e

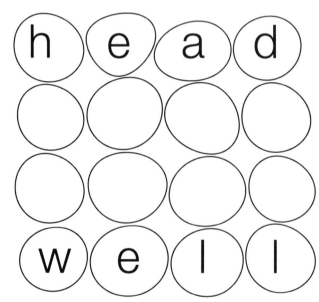

h e a d

w e l l

h a n d

b e n t

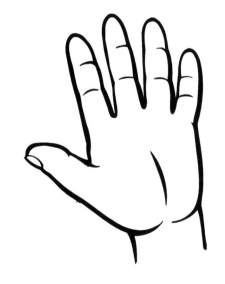

www.ricpublications.com.au   R.I.C. Publications®

STEPPING STONES

Change the following words, one letter at a time, to make the last word shown. Each step must be a proper word! If you can do it in even fewer steps - well done!

p i l e

( ) ( ) ( ) ( )

( ) ( ) ( ) ( )

h a l t

g a t e

( ) ( ) ( ) ( )

( ) ( ) ( ) ( )

c o m e

s h o e

( ) ( ) ( ) ( )

( ) ( ) ( ) ( )

s t e p

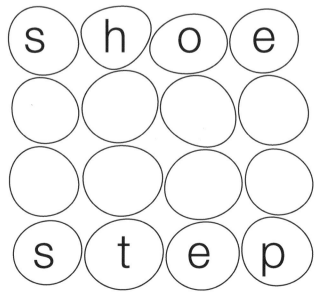

STEPPING STONES

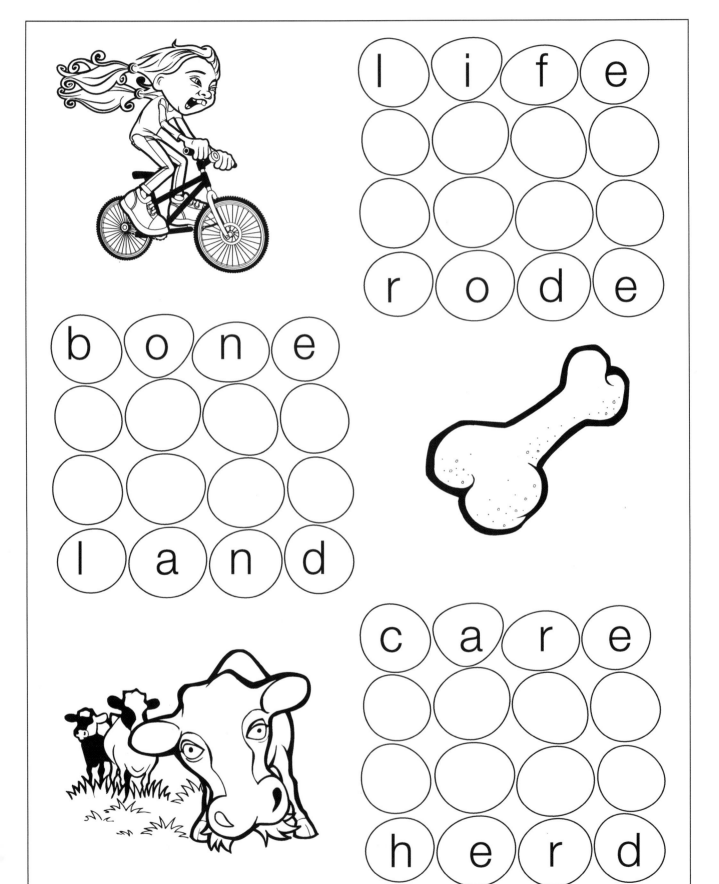

l i f e

r o d e

b o n e

l a n d

c a r e

h e r d

Name: _____

Date: _____

These exercises are to practise classifying information into groups.
Circle the word which does not belong in the set and write it down in the space provided.
Then explain why it doesn't belong.

A.

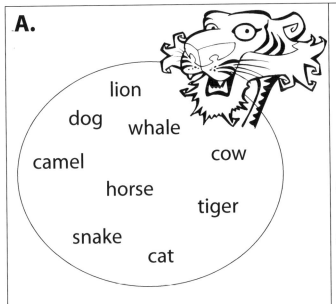

lion

dog   whale

camel   cow

horse

tiger

snake

cat

Odd word out: _____

_____

It does not belong in the set because **all the rest:**

_____

_____

B.

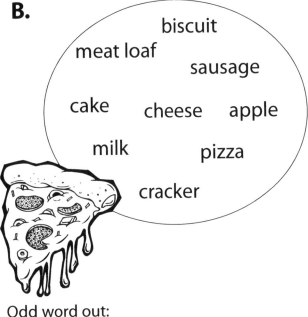

biscuit

meat loaf   sausage

cake   cheese   apple

milk   pizza

cracker

Odd word out: _____

_____

It does not belong in the set because **all the rest:**

_____

_____

C.

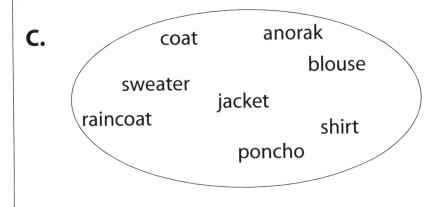

coat   anorak

blouse

sweater   jacket

raincoat   shirt

poncho

Odd word out: _____

It does not belong in the set because **all the rest:**

_____

Find the set

Name: _____

Date: _____

D.

cotton

nylon   satin   corduroy

canvas   silk

wool

velvet

linen

Odd word out: _____

It does not belong in the set because **all the rest:**

_____

E.

CHALLENGE! Each of the activities above has **another** possible answer. Can you find it?

A. Odd word out: _____

It does not belong in the set because **all the rest:**

_____

B. Odd word out: _____

It does not belong in the set because **all the rest:**

_____

C. Odd word out: _____

It does not belong in the set because **all the rest:**

_____

D. Odd word out: _____

It does not belong in the set because **all the rest:**

_____

These exercises are to practise classifying information into groups.
Circle the word which does not belong in the set and write it down in the space provided.
Then explain why it doesn't belong.

A.

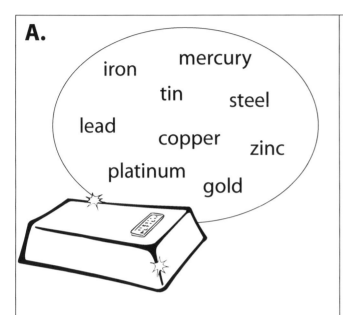

iron   mercury

tin   steel

lead   copper   zinc

platinum   gold

Odd word out:

_____

It does not belong in the set because **all the rest:**

_____

_____

B.

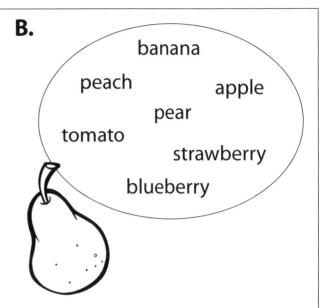

banana

peach   apple

pear

tomato   strawberry

blueberry

Odd word out:

_____

It does not belong in the set because **all the rest:**

_____

_____

C.

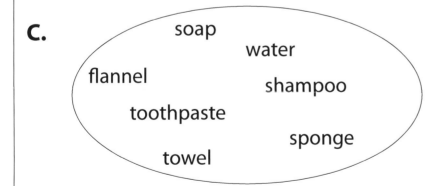

soap

water

flannel   shampoo

toothpaste

sponge

towel

Odd word out:_____

It does not belong in the set because **all the rest:**

_____

Find the set

D.

rowing   cricket

squash

tennis

rugby

basketball   gymnastics

netball

Odd word out: _____

It does not belong in the set because **all the rest:**

_____

E.

CHALLENGE! Each of the activities above has **another** possible answer. Can you find it?

A. Odd word out: _____

It does not belong in the set because **all the rest:**

_____

B. Odd word out: _____

It does not belong in the set because **all the rest:**

_____

C. Odd word out: _____

It does not belong in the set because **all the rest:**

_____

D. Odd word out: _____

It does not belong in the set because **all the rest:**

_____

Name: _____

Date: _____

These exercises are to practise classifying information into groups.
Circle the word which does not belong in the set and write it down in the space provided.
Then explain why it doesn't belong.

A.

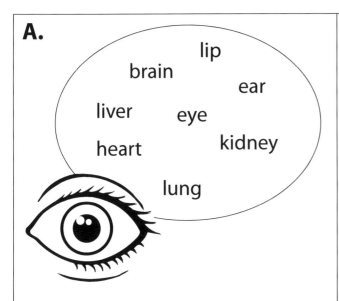

lip
brain
ear
liver   eye
heart   kidney
lung

Odd word out:

_____

It does not belong in the set because **all the rest:**

_____

_____

B.

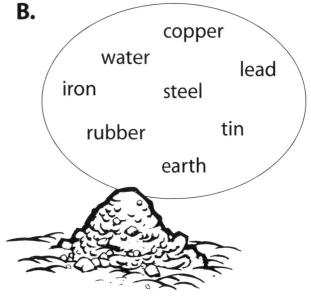

copper
water
lead
iron   steel
rubber   tin
earth

Odd word out:

_____

It does not belong in the set because **all the rest:**

_____

_____

C.

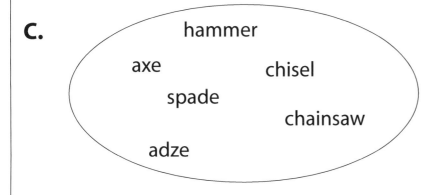

hammer
axe   chisel
spade   chainsaw
adze

Odd word out: _____

It does not belong in the set because **all the rest:**

_____

Find the set

Name: _____

Date: _____

D.

savoury

sweet

sour

spicy

slimy

bitter

salty

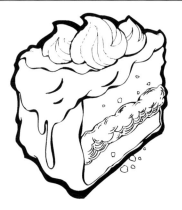

Odd word out: _____

It does not belong in the set because **all the rest:**

_____

E.

CHALLENGE! Each of the activities above has **another** possible answer. Can you find it?

A. Odd word out: _____

It does not belong in the set because **all the rest:**

_____

B. Odd word out: _____

It does not belong in the set because **all the rest:**

_____

C. Odd word out: _____

It does not belong in the set because **all the rest:**

_____

D. Odd word out: _____

It does not belong in the set because **all the rest:**

_____

Name:

Date:

You might not agree with some of these statements as you work through these exercises – but the main point is to learn Venn diagrams, so let's assume that all of them are true. Use the patterns in the key boxes to shade carefully inside the Venn circles to show:

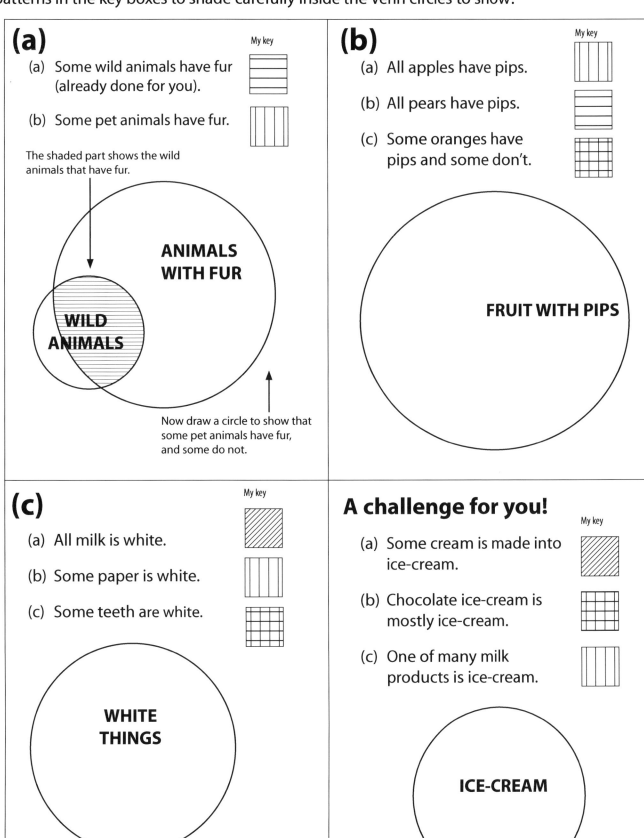

(a)

(a) Some wild animals have fur (already done for you).

(b) Some pet animals have fur.

My key

The shaded part shows the wild animals that have fur.

ANIMALS WITH FUR

WILD ANIMALS

Now draw a circle to show that some pet animals have fur, and some do not.

(b)

(a) All apples have pips.

(b) All pears have pips.

(c) Some oranges have pips and some don't.

My key

FRUIT WITH PIPS

(c)

(a) All milk is white.

(b) Some paper is white.

(c) Some teeth are white.

My key

WHITE THINGS

A challenge for you!

(a) Some cream is made into ice-cream.

(b) Chocolate ice-cream is mostly ice-cream.

(c) One of many milk products is ice-cream.

My key

ICE-CREAM

Venn diagrams

Next, you need to think carefully about the **SIZE** of the part you overlap. This gives people information too!

Look at the first diagram. Then, draw and shade in carefully inside the Venn circles using the patterns in the key boxes to show:

Name: _____

Date: _____

(a)

(a) Most wild animals have fur.

(b) About half of all pet animals have fur.

My key

(a) Because most of the circle is INSIDE the 'Animals with fur' part, this means that MOST wild animals have fur.

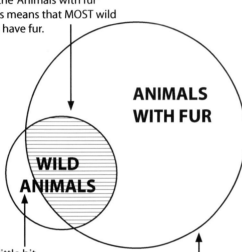

ANIMALS WITH FUR

WILD ANIMALS

(b) So this little bit means that only A SMALL NUMBER of wild animals don't have fur.

(c) Now draw a circle to show that about HALF of pet animals DO have fur, and half of pet animals DON'T have fur. Think carefully!

(b)

(a) All apples have pips.

(b) All lemons have pips.

(c) Most oranges have pips and a few don't.

My key

This time, think hard how to show that nearly all oranges have pips and that only a few types don't.

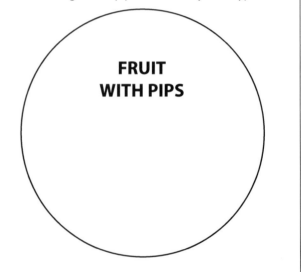

FRUIT WITH PIPS

(c)

My key

(a) All fresh milk is white.
(b) About half of all paper is white.
(c) About two-thirds of teeth are white.

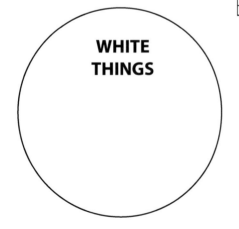

WHITE THINGS

A challenge for you!

(a) About one-third of all PLANTS are trees.

(b) About half of <u>all</u> trees are <u>deciduous</u> (lose their leaves); the other half are evergreen.

My key

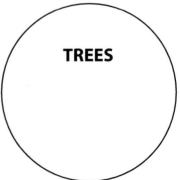

TREES

- DID YOU MAKE SURE that you didn't leave any space for trees that are <u>neither</u> deciduous <u>nor</u> evergreen— because there is no such thing …!

Venn diagrams

Using these attributes: **parents, women, tall**
use the patterns in the key boxes to shade carefully
inside the Venn circles to show:

(a)

(a) All mothers. (HINT: draw a line first)

(b) All tall parents.

(c) Tall fathers.

My key

HUMAN PARENTS   **TALL PEOPLE**

(b)

HINT: you need to draw a LINE here before you shade in, as it's exactly half and half …

(a) Men who are fathers (parents).

(b) Men who are not fathers.

(c) A FEW young adults are parents.

(HINT: You need to draw a new circle—place it carefully!)

My key

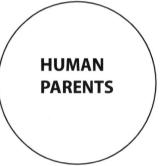

HUMAN PARENTS

(c)

(a) All tall parents.

(b) Tall people who are not parents.

(c) All mothers
     (THINK: Draw a line or a circle?)

My key

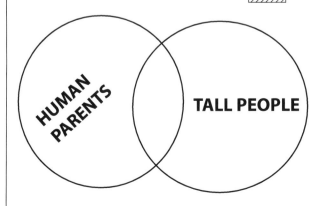

HUMAN PARENTS   **TALL PEOPLE**

A challenge for you!

Draw and label a circle for all tall things (including people).

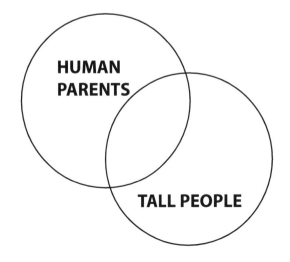

HUMAN PARENTS

TALL PEOPLE

Name: _____

Date: _____

Using these attributes: **hot, green, foods,** use the patterns in the key boxes to shade carefully inside the Venn circles to show:

(a)

(a) All foods.

(b) Foods which are not hot.

My key

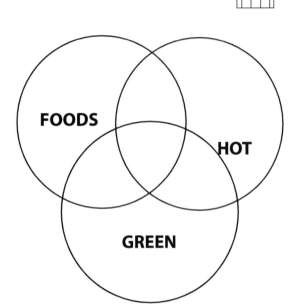

(b)

(a) All green foods.

(b) Hot green foods (such as cooked broccoli).

(c) Green foods that are NOT hot (such as lettuce).

My key

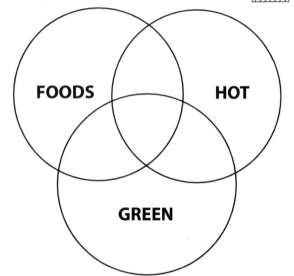

(c)

(a) All hot foods which are NOT green.

(b) All foods which are NOT hot and NOT green.

My key

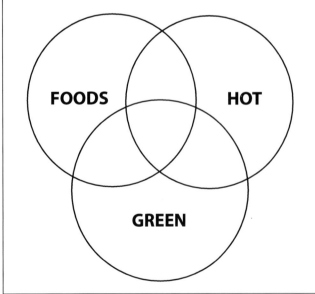

A challenge for you!

Where would you put a little circle for:

(a) Trees?

(b) Carrots just out of the pot?

(c) Lime ice-cream?

My key

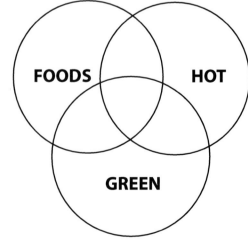

Name: _____

Date: _____

Some of these are tricky!

Look at the underlined word. All of the other words except one belong in the set.

Find the odd one out!

Copy the word neatly on the answer line, or in your book. **Give your reason** for your choice!

---

1. cat

table	dog
bird	fish

odd one out:

table

reason:

the rest are all alive

---

2. pear

orange	tree
apple	cherry

odd one out:

_____

reason:

_____

_____

Name: _____

Date: _____

3. <u>finger</u>

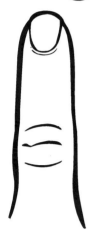

nail	thumb
ear	ring

odd one out:

_____

reason:

_____

_____

4. <u>pencil</u>

truck	paper
rubber	crayon

odd one out:

_____

reason:

_____

_____

5. <u>carrot</u>

potato	apple
beetroot	onion

odd one out:

_____

reason:

_____

_____

Name: _____

Date: _____

Look at the underlined word.

Then find the best word from the other choices that **goes with it** to make a pair.

Copy the word neatly on the answer line, or in your book.

Examples: cup *and* saucer; bread *and* butter

---

1. hand *and:*

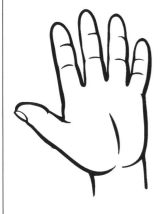

shoe	glove
sock	wet

answer:

hand and glove _____

---

2. knife *and:*

hand	sock
fork	dog

answer:

knife and _____

Name:

Date:

3. <u>soap</u> *and:*

sky	ant
water	clear

answer:

soap and _____

4. <u>stamp</u> *and:*

shoe	letter
wood	box

answer:

stamp and _____

5. <u>ring</u> *and:*

apple	book
money	finger

answer:

ring and _____

Name:

Date:

Look at the underlined word.

Then find the best word from the other choices that **goes with it** to make a pair.

Copy the word neatly on the answer line, or in your book.

1. apple

| orange | bed |
| twig | big |

answer:

apple and

2. rain

| toast | white |
| umbrella | farm |

answer:

rain and

Name:

Date:

3. <u>sheep</u>

pink	cow
tree	fish

answer:

sheep and _____

4. <u>cat</u>

shiny	red
dog	ring

answer:

cat and _____

5. <u>spider</u>

big	eye
floor	web

answer:

spider and _____

Name: _____

Date: _____

Look at the underlined word.

Then find the best word from the other choices that **shows what it is used for.**

Copy the word neatly on the answer line, or in your book.

1. spade *is used to:*

| pear | handle |
| shed | dig |

answer:

a spade is used to dig

2. knife

| toast | cut |
| sharp | metal |

answer:

a knife is used to

Name: _____

Date: _____

3. <u>needle</u>

sew	paper
dress	sharp

answer:

a needle is used to _____

4. <u>pencil</u>

sharp	pen
write	letter

answer:

a pencil is used to _____

5. <u>cup</u>

eye	think
drink	eat

answer:

a cup is used to _____

www.ricpublications.com.au   R.I.C. Publications®

Name:

Date:

Look at the underlined word.

Then find the best word from the other choices that **shows the opposite.**

Copy the word neatly on the answer line, or in your book.

1. <u>hard</u>

soft	thin
kitten	wood

answer:

_____

2. <u>wild</u>

side	cat
tame	tiger

answer:

_____

Name: _____

Date: _____

3. <u>kind</u>

wild	kitten
me	cruel

answer: _____

_____

4. <u>cold</u>

wet	cool
hot	summer

answer: _____

_____

5. <u>wet</u>

dry	water
hot	rain

answer: _____

_____

Name: _____

Date: _____

21

Outside the shop

Number of ideas [ ]

Original ideas [ ]

Final total [ ]

Your aim: To use creative and analytical thinking, by looking at a situation from different angles in order to find possible alternative or underlying problems.

Method: Study the illustration. There could be many different problems rather than just the one which is immediately apparent to you. Put on your thinking cap and see how many possible problems you can list, which could explain the situation in the picture.

Sample responses:

1. His shoes have been superglued™ together.

2. He's broken the shop window.

3. He's lost his wallet.

4. His shoelaces have been tied together.

5. He's actually inside the shop and he's a plain, tired-out assistant.

6. He's tripped over those pebbles in the picture.

7. He's been waiting more than five minutes.

8. The sale's sold out.

9. He found he can't return a sale item.

10. He's just sitting on the footpath.

11. There's been a riot outside and he was hit on the head.

12. He's waiting for his mum to come with money.

13. He's acting in a movie and waiting for the next 'take'.

14. The black 'shadows' are from another dimension and are invading his mind (hence hands on head).

Outside the shop

Your aim: To use creative and analytical thinking by looking at a situation from different angles in order to find possible alternative or underlying problems.

Method: Study the illustration. There could be many different problems rather than just the one which is immediately apparent to you. Put on your thinking cap and see how many possible problems you can list which could explain the situation in the picture.

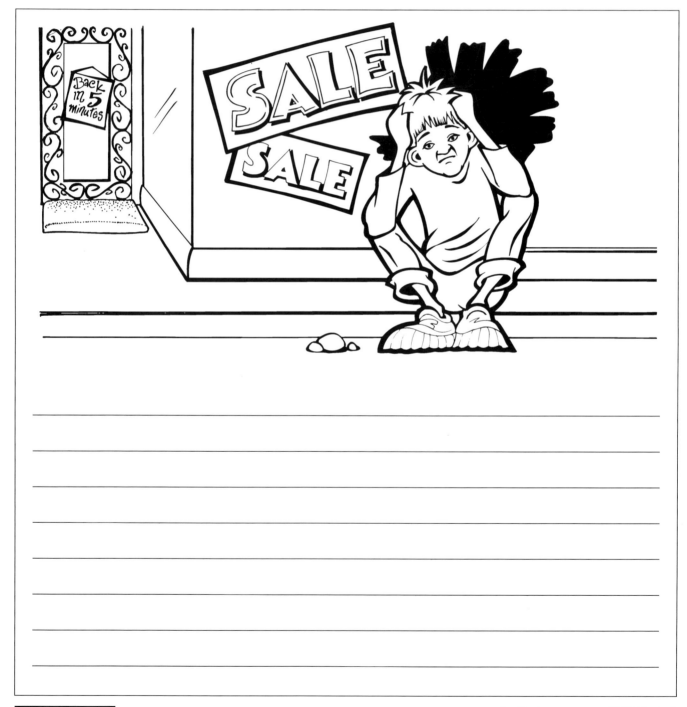

Name:

Date:

Number of ideas ☐

Original ideas ☐

Final total ☐

The car

Your aim: To use creative and analytical thinking by looking at a situation from different angles in order to find possible alternative or underlying problems.

Method: Study the illustration. There could be many different problems rather than just the one which is immediately apparent to you. Put on your thinking cap and see how many possible problems you can list which could explain the situation in the picture.

_____

_____

_____

_____

_____

_____

_____

www.ricpublications.com.au   R.I.C. Publications®

spotting problems

THINK OUTSIDE THE SQUARE

Name:

Date:

Number of ideas

Original ideas

Final total

Dad's cross

Your aim: To use creative and analytical thinking by looking at a situation from different angles in order to find possible alternative or underlying problems.

Method: Study the illustration. There could be many different problems rather than just the one which is immediately apparent to you. Put on your thinking cap and see how many possible problems you can list which could explain the situation in the picture.

_____

_____

_____

_____

_____

_____

_____

spotting problems

THINK OUTSIDE THE SQUARE

Number of ideas ▢   Original ideas ▢   Final total ▢

24

Name:

Date:

Late with homework

UNDERLYING PROBLEMS

AIM:

To use analytical and creative thinking to find underlying problems relating to one overall problem.

TASK

1. Many different underlying problems can be lumped under one main problem. In a group, BRAINSTORM as many different underlying problems as you can which could be causing someone your age to keep handing in homework late.

votes

www.ricpublications.com.au   R.I.C. Publications®

2. **VOTE** in your group with a show of hands for problems with late homework that each of you personally has experienced. Enter the score in the boxes on the right of each underlying problem.

3. **RANK** the underlying problems by entering the highest-scoring three on the lines below.

The three most common underlying problems causing homework to be handed in late are:

I st _____

_____

2nd _____

_____

3rd _____

_____

4. **NOW SUGGEST SOLUTIONS** for these three problem situations:

_____

_____

_____

_____

_____

_____

_____

_____

_____

25

Name:

Date:

Put-downs

UNDERLYING PROBLEMS

AIM:

To use analytical and creative thinking to find underlying problems relating to one overall problem.

TASK

1. Many different underlying problems can be lumped under one main problem. In a group, BRAINSTORM as many different underlying problems as you can which explain why people your age may be giving 'put-downs' to others. You may have felt like giving a put-down but restrained yourself *(great self-control!)*, but think about what caused you to feel like that.

votes

2. VOTE in your group with a show of hands for put-downs that each of you personally has experienced. Enter the score in the boxes on the right of each underlying problem.

3. RANK the underlying problems by entering the highest-scoring three on the lines below.

The three most common underlying problems with put-downs that our group found are:

1st _____

_____

2nd _____

_____

3rd _____

_____

4. NOW SUGGEST SOLUTIONS for these three problem situations:

_____

_____

_____

_____

_____

_____

_____

_____

_____

_____

_____

26 Name: _____

Date: _____

AIM:

To use analytical and creative thinking to find underlying problems relating to one overall problem.

TASK

1. Many different underlying problems can be lumped under one main problem. In a group, BRAINSTORM as many different underlying problems as you can why a brother or sister may be annoying you.

votes

_____ ☐

_____ ☐

_____ ☐

_____ ☐

_____ ☐

_____ ☐

_____ ☐

_____ ☐

_____ ☐

_____ ☐

_____ ☐

_____ ☐

_____ ☐

2. **VOTE** in your group with a show of hands for problems with brothers or sisters that each of you personally has experienced. Enter the score in the boxes on the right of each underlying problem.

3. **RANK** the underlying problems by entering the highest-scoring three on the lines below.

> **The three most common underlying problems with brothers or sisters being annoying that our group found are:**
>
> 1st _____
>
> _____
>
> 2nd _____
>
> _____
>
> 3rd _____
>
> _____

4. **NOW SUGGEST SOLUTIONS** for these three problem situations:

_____

_____

_____

_____

_____

_____

_____

_____

_____

_____

Name: _____

Date: _____

'WOW – thanks – the PERFECT GIFT!'

Here's your chance to practise using criteria in real life.

You need to make up criteria for people to use before they choose you a present. Showing them this list might even help them to recognise that there are other alternatives too!

1. Discuss the following questions before you make up your criteria:

    •   Is anyone disturbed easily by noise in your family? How can some gifts avoid this?

    •   Some gifts are boring after 2 or 3 days – why is this?

    •   What makes you treasure a gift for a long time?

    •   Some gifts delight you even though they weren't expensive – what is it you like about them?

    •   Do you like doing things on your own or with others?

    •   What if something breaks or doesn't work properly?

2. BRAINSTORM as a class all the criteria you now think are important for a gift for yourself. Then choose the five most important to you and write them in the grid below. Then, working ACROSS the rows, compare each gift. Score each out of 10. Think carefully!

Criteria for a present for: _____					
1.					
2.					
3.					
4.					
5.					
Totals					

My best idea turned out to be: _____

Share your list with your family – they should be impressed with the thought you've given to this … (and they might have other criteria they'd like to add!).

These are one-syllable rhyming pairs, along with a definition or clue for them. See if you can complete them!

Hint: work through the alphabet!

1. obese feline **f a t   c a t**

2. canine swamp ☐☐☐ ☐☐☐

3. skinny object with sharp point ☐☐☐☐ ☐☐☐

4. primary-coloured body part ☐☐☐ ☐☐☐☐

5. amphibian route ☐☐☐☐ ☐☐☐☐

· ·

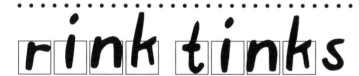

Name:

Date:

28

These are one-syllable rhyming pairs, along with a definition or clue for them. See if you can complete them!

Hint: work through the alphabet!

1. obese feline **f a t   c a t**

2. canine swamp ☐☐☐ ☐☐☐

3. skinny object with sharp point ☐☐☐☐ ☐☐☐

4. primary-coloured body part ☐☐☐ ☐☐☐☐

5. amphibian route ☐☐☐☐ ☐☐☐☐

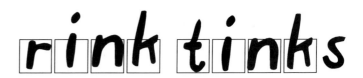

These are one-syllable rhyming pairs, along with a definition or clue for them. See if you can complete them!

1. skinny sharp object ☐☐☐ ☐☐☐

2. squashed item to go on your head ☐☐☐☐ ☐☐☐

3. a broad playground item ☐☐☐☐ ☐☐☐☐

4. unhappy father ☐☐☐ ☐☐☐

5. stinging insect urine ☐☐☐ ☐☐☐

. . . .

29 Name: _____
Date: _____

rink tinks

These are one-syllable rhyming pairs, along with a definition or clue for them. See if you can complete them!

1. skinny sharp object ☐☐☐ ☐☐☐

2. squashed item to go on your head ☐☐☐☐ ☐☐☐

3. a broad playground item ☐☐☐☐ ☐☐☐☐

4. unhappy father ☐☐☐ ☐☐☐

5. stinging insect urine ☐☐☐ ☐☐☐

These are one-syllable rhyming pairs, along with a definition or clue for them. See if you can complete them!

1. drinking container for a small dog ☐☐☐ ☐☐☐

2. unruly young person ☐☐☐☐ ☐☐☐☐☐

3. plaything for a young male ☐☐☐ ☐☐☐

4. grey matter on a
   means of transport ☐☐☐☐☐☐☐☐☐☐

5. dessert for a type of common insect ☐☐☐ ☐☐☐

. . . .

rink tinks

Name: _____

Date: _____

30

These are one-syllable rhyming pairs, along with a definition or clue for them. See if you can complete them!

1. drinking container for a small dog ☐☐☐ ☐☐☐

2. unruly young person ☐☐☐☐ ☐☐☐☐☐

3. plaything for a young male ☐☐☐ ☐☐☐

4. grey matter on a
   means of transport ☐☐☐☐☐☐☐☐☐☐

5. dessert for a type of common insect ☐☐☐ ☐☐☐

Name:

Date:

rinky tinky

These are 2-syllable rhyming words. Find rhyming words to make the rinky-tinky.

This would make a great wall-display and get some head-scratching going on!

1. cheerful daddy ☐☐☐☐☐☐ ☐☐☐☐☐

2. liquid cash ☐☐☐☐☐ ☐☐☐☐☐

3. glove for a young cat

☐☐☐☐☐☐ ☐☐☐☐☐

4. hilarious rabbit ☐☐☐☐☐ ☐☐☐☐☐

5. a boxer who's been on a diet and weighs less

☐☐☐☐☐☐☐ ☐☐☐☐☐☐

· ·

31

Name:

Date:

rinky tinky

These are 2-syllable rhyming words. Find rhyming words to make the rinky-tinky.

This would make a great wall-display and get some head-scratching going on!

1. cheerful daddy ☐☐☐☐☐☐ ☐☐☐☐☐

2. liquid cash ☐☐☐☐☐ ☐☐☐☐☐

3. glove for a young cat

☐☐☐☐☐☐ ☐☐☐☐☐

4. hilarious rabbit ☐☐☐☐☐ ☐☐☐☐☐

5. a boxer who's been on a diet and weighs less

☐☐☐☐☐☐☐ ☐☐☐☐☐☐

BRAIN BUSTER

Your product:

Shoes with velcro™ soles
(and no, realistically, people can't walk up walls with them)

Your task:

1. Brainstorm uses for your product, with a group.

Names of our design and marketing team:

_____   _____

_____   _____

Brainstormed uses for our product:

_____

_____

_____

_____

_____

_____

_____

_____

2. Each choose YOUR personal favourite, and create a name for your product.

3. Design a logo.

4. Make an advertisement for your product. Remember the four golden rules:

(a) Catch their attention – use an attention grabber!

(b) Give them a couple of facts to get them interested in reading further.

(c) Give details about its uses.

(d) Tell them why they NEED this product, and where they can get it.

5. Invent a jingle for the radio, which you can sing to a well-known tune.

Your product:

Peel-off food varnish

Your task:

1. Brainstorm uses for your product with a group.

Names of our design and marketing team:

_____   _____

_____   _____

Brainstormed uses for our product:

_____

_____

_____

_____

_____

_____

_____

2. Each choose YOUR personal favourite and create a name for your product.

3. Design a logo.

4. Make an advertisement for your product. Remember the four golden rules:

    (a) Catch their attention – use an attention grabber!

    (b) Give them a couple of facts to get them interested in reading further.

    (c) Give details about its uses.

    (d) Tell them why they NEED this product, and where they can get it.

5. Invent a jingle for the radio, which you can sing to a well-known tune.

Your product:

Clothes that dissolve in water

Your task:

1. Brainstorm uses for your product, with a group.

Names of our design and marketing team:

_____   _____

_____   _____

Brainstormed uses for our product:

_____

_____

_____

_____

_____

_____

_____

_____

2. Each choose YOUR personal favourite and create a name for your product.

3. Design a logo.

4. Make an advertisement for your product. Remember the four golden rules:

   (a) Catch their attention – use an attention grabber!

   (b) Give them a couple of facts to get them interested in reading further.

   (c) Give details about its uses.

   (d) Tell them why they NEED this product, and where they can get it.

5. Invent a jingle for the radio, which you can sing to a well-known tune.

Your product:

Inflatable hats

Your task:

1. Brainstorm uses for your product with a group.

Names of our design and marketing team:

_____   _____

_____   _____

Brainstormed uses for our product:

_____

_____

_____

_____

_____

_____

_____

2. Each choose YOUR personal favourite, and create a name for your product.

3. Design a logo.

4. Make an advertisement for your product. Remember the four golden rules:

(a) Catch their attention – use an attention grabber!

(b) Give them a couple of facts to get them interested in reading further.

(c) Give details about its uses.

(d) Tell them why they NEED this product and where they can get it.

5. Invent a jingle for the radio, which you can sing to a well-known tune.

Design a way of getting people on and off buses without the buses having to stop.

Realistic practical	
Imaginary impractical	

Write a few sentences to describe how your solution works. Then draw a diagram of it, with labelled parts.

_____

_____

_____

_____

_____

Name: _____ Date: _____

Design a new layout for your classroom. It should be realistic and practical, and improve something specific in your present room.

Realistic practical	
Imaginary impractical	

Write a few sentences to describe how your solution works. Then draw a diagram of it, with labelled parts.

_____

_____

_____

_____

_____

_____

www.ricpublications.com.au   R.I.C. Publications®

Design a new bicycle.
It should improve on current bicycles in some way.

Realistic practical	
Imaginary impractical	

Write a few sentences to describe how your solution works. Then draw a diagram of it, with labelled parts.

_____

_____

_____

_____

_____

_____

Name: _____   Date: _____

**Design the perfect candy.
Use ingredients which are easy to get should you actually
try to make this treat for your classmates ...**

| Realistic practical | |
| Imaginary impractical | |

Write a few sentences to describe how your solution works. Then draw a diagram of it, with labelled parts.

_____

_____

_____

_____

_____

www.ricpublications.com.au   R.I.C. Publications®

9 **Find the set page 19**

A. snake – all the rest are mammals

camel – rest need to eat regularly

whale – rest live on land

B. milk – rest are solids

apple – rest are generally processed

C. poncho – rest have sleeves

anorak – rest don't keep out wind

blouse – rest are unisex

D. nylon – rest are natural (not synthetic)

silk – rest are picked or sheared (not excreted)

10 **Find the set page 21**

A. mercury – rest are solid

steel – rest are raw (not composites/compounds)

gold – rest rust/tarnish

B. peach – rest have seeds (not pit)

banana – rest skins eaten too

blueberry – rest have an 'a'

C. water – rest are solids

toothpaste – rest are non-specific for cleaning

towel – rest don't remove water

D. rowing – rest are on land

tennis – rest not divided by a net

gymnastics – rest performed without mats

11 **Find the set page 23**

A. lip – rest are organs

brain – rest can be transplanted

B. rubber – rest are conductors of electricity

water – rest are solids

C. chainsaw – rest are fuel-less (powered by humans)

hammer – rest are for cutting/slicing

D. slimy – rest are textures

bitter – rest begin with 's'

12 **Venn diagrams page 25**

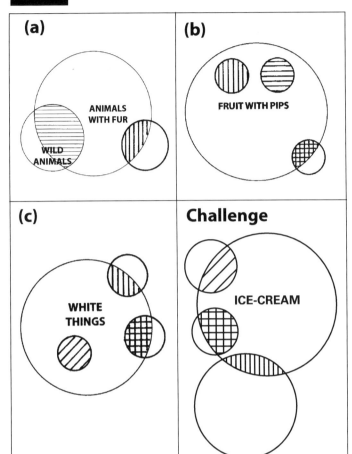

13 **Venn diagrams page 26**

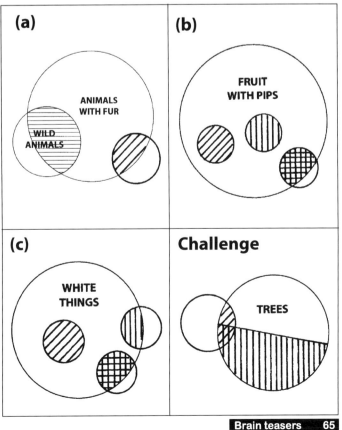

answers continued

14   Venn diagrams page 27

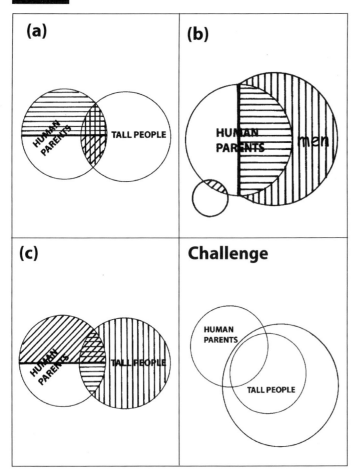

(a)   **(b)**   **(c)**   **Challenge**

15   Venn diagrams page 28

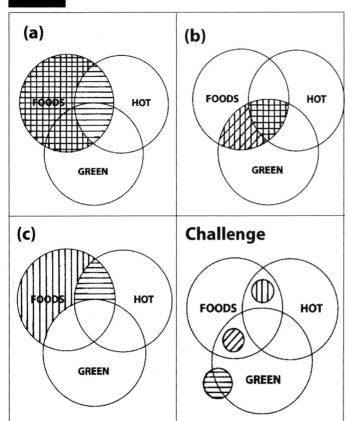

(a)   **(b)**   **(c)**   **Challenge**

16   odd one out pages 29–30

Accept any other reasonable answer

1. table (rest are all alive)
2. tree (rest are all fruit)
3. ear (rest all belong on your hand)
4. truck (rest are all for drawing/ writing)
5. apple (rest are all vegetables)

17   best pair pages 31–32

1. glove
2. fork
3. water
4. letter
5. finger

18   best pair pages 33–34

1. pear
2. cloud
3. cow
4. dog
5. web

19   is used for pages 35–36

1. dig
2. cut
3. sew
4. write
5. drink

20   find the opposite pages 37–38

1. soft
2. tame
3. cruel
4. hot
5. dry

www.ricpublications.com.au   R.I.C. Publications®